Th
dat
cha

Combining barley on a large arable farm in north Warwickshire.

Colin Shaw

FARMWORK

Men and Women on the Land

With a foreword by Phil Drabble

Chatto & Windus · London

First published in 1988
by Chatto & Windus Ltd
30 Bedford Square
London WC1B 3RP

A CIP catalogue record for this book
is available from the British Library.

ISBN 0 7011 3299 X

Photoset by Rowland Phototypesetting Ltd
Bury St Edmunds, Suffolk
Printed in Great Britain by
Butler and Tanner Ltd, Frome, Somerset

ACKNOWLEDGEMENTS

I would like to thank all who made this project possible,
especially, West Midlands Arts for funding the photography and
research, ICI Fertilizers for funding the production and tour of
the exhibitions (I am especially indebted to Robert Sentence of
ICI Fertilizers), the NFU, the Royal Agricultural Society of
England, Hilary Laurie of Chatto & Windus for her foresight and
patience, and all of the farmers and farm workers who agreed to
my presence on their farms and the inevitable inconvenience that
it caused. Without their cooperation the project would have been
rather difficult. Last, but by no means least, I would like to thank
Hazel; without her this project would certainly not have been
completed.

For those interested in the technical details, I used a Mamiya 645
camera and lenses of 35, 45, 55, 80, 150 and 210mm focal length.
The film was either Ilford FP4 rated at 125 ASA or Kodak Tri-X
rated at either 400, 800 or 1600 ASA. The original prints were
printed on Agfa Record Rapid which was toned to slightly cool
off the image. All prints were processed to full archival standards
and mounted on acid free board.
C.S.

Foreword by Phil Drabble

Having long passed my three score years and ten, I have been able to watch the scale and pattern of farmwork change beyond recognition. During my summer holidays from prep school, my great delight was to ride on the back of the lead horse, in a team of three, pulling a 'binder' which cut the corn and left it lying in the field as rows of neatly tied-up sheaves.

Farm labourers followed us round the field, 'stooking' (or stacking) the sheaves in stooks of eight or ten sheaves, to dry in the wind and sun. They were then carted to the rickyard and built into ricks, to await the arrival of an itinerant threshing machine crew who threshed the corn and left the straw as bedding for farm stock.

This book of superb photographs by Colin Shaw shows a very different picture of the countryside, because such methods were very labour-intensive and wages have escalated till any farmer who used such antiquated methods would soon be out of business. In my young days there was a farm labourer to roughly every fifty acres. A modern thousand acre farm employs a foreman and two or three farm workers – who would be insulted if you called them labourers!

There is nothing surprising about this because the countryside changed in the past, it is changing now and nothing we can do will stop it changing in the future.

Our distant ancestors nibbled clearings in the forest to provide better grazing for their stock. Their descendants enlarged the clearings into farms, much of which was common land, and for centuries the arable land was tilled by horses which still held sway when I was young, for I can remember the first tractor coming to our village.

The technological change, which Colin Shaw portrays so vividly, was really sired during the last war. Airfields and factories literally appeared overnight. It was vital that they did because we were fighting for our way of life and, when men are really up against it, they think fast and work hard. Giant bulldozers and juggernauts were invented which could shift as much earth in a day as men with tractors could have accomplished in weeks.

When the urgency of war was over, the same brains produced combine harvesters instead of tanks, chemical pesticides to annihilate insect pests instead of soldiers, and multi-furrow ploughs instead of more dramatic earthmoving equipment.

Colin Shaw's photographs illustrate this phase of agricultural change to perfection. The multi skills of craftsmen, who could use hand tools to hedge and ditch or hoe or milk cows by hand, became as obsolete as good manners at a football match, and the survivors of such trades seem equally out of place. His portrait of market gardeners with hands wizened by frost, picking sprouts in a snowy field, must seem as much of an anachronism as the term 'hotache' for frostbitten fingers they probably never experienced.

The pictures in this book really speak for themselves. They tell the tale of a technological revolution which has literally changed the face of our countryside in a single generation.

Horses and primitive tractors could manoeuvre neatly in fields of five acres or so, which had been ideal when the venerable rotation of crops, to provide natural fertility, was in fashion. Rich muck was carted from stockyards and spread, by hand, upon the fields. Corn was grown and undersown with grass or clover, so that the land could be rested by grazing with stock which left a blanket of their own fresh muck, as payment for the luxury of living naturally.

In the rural world this book encapsulates, farming has become Big Business instead of a way of life. Craftsmen now have to add 'skilled mechanic' to their job application forms. Farm managers calculate the rations for their cows and sheep in the abracadabra of computer jargon.

The picture of a bare field, apparently stretching to infinity, with a Tractor Operator (not waggoner or farm labourer) about to groom the land for its next crop made me wonder how I would feel if I could not escape from a field of infinite size until I had ploughed countless identical furrows across it! Or seeing numberless – but serially numbered – cows filing in and out of a milking parlour would make counting sheep, as a cure for insomnia, seem kindergarten stuff.

Colin Shaw has painted his subject, warts and all. His human portraits are quite superb, for the men on farms have not changed much, however revolutionary the methods used may be. Such brilliant photography does drive home the fact that intensive stock keeping and prairie farming do have warts which almost amount to a rash. A morning jabbing sheep with hypodermic needles, as a necessary control for ailments caused by close confinement, seems a high price to pay to make such 'enterprises' profitable. And sows, cramped in stalls too narrow for them to turn round, scarcely equate with my memories when farmers and their labourers took pride in the fact that the British were the kindest stockmen in the world.

This searching portrayal of modern farming suggests to me that the phase it records will be looked back on, in future, as the record of yet another *changing* face of agriculture. A face which will fade. The machines our boffins have devised might well be selfdestructive. They are so super-efficient that they have not only met our needs but produced surplus corn mountains and milk lakes and butter bogs which are bankrupting us. And the ruthless test for Big Business is that what is not profitable is for the high jump. Add to that the fact that modern machinery shown in this book is so expensive that only the very largest farms can afford such capital-intensive equipment. It is not easy to make a machine costing five or even six figures set off its capital cost with only a few days a year productive work. So the future trend may well be to have contractors, who own the equipment, to do the work, which will, in turn, allow a return to smaller, *family* farms, concentrating on quality instead of quantity production. Colin Shaw is still young enough, with luck, to record the next link in the endless chain of change, when machines become, once more, our slaves instead of our masters.

Introduction

Growing up in a small Warwickshire village, it was impossible to ignore the day to day activities of farming. My memories of childhood are dominated by the freedom of a rural existence and the realities of living in an agricultural community: walking in meadows that had never been ploughed; watching the gangs of women with their prams, wellington boots, headscarves and buckets waiting to go potato picking, then experiencing for myself the inevitable backache of the job; learning to drive a tractor; watching and trying hand-milking on a friend's small holding; helping to churn the cream to butter by hand, and enjoying the reward of fresh watercress sandwiches.

All of this was seasoned with the advice and country wisdom of my father. He started life as a farm worker in Lincolnshire; a steam traction engine was the first vehicle he ever drove. 'Never walk across a ploughed field,' he would say, 'even if the footpath goes straight across the middle . . . always be wary of male animals, especially pigs! . . . Never go in a field if a cow has just calved; they can be worse than bulls.' My father left farm work because of low pay and the demands of a growing family. I never knew him when he was a farm worker, but his country wisdom remained and was a constant source of knowledge during my childhood.

During the 1950s it was not unusual for villagers to keep a 'cottage pig' and a few hens. My father was no exception and I well remember riding on the back of a huge Middle White called Sally. We watched her farrow and saw the piglets feed and grow; then they were gone. The day that Sally went, father was very upset; I remember the pots of home made brawn and cuts of meat in my grandmother's kitchen. He never had another pig.

I enjoyed the regular trips to our field and always marvelled at my father's skill. I remember watching as he carefully loaded eggs into an incubator and filled and lit the paraffin heater. I recall him explaining patiently that they needed warmth to hatch, and that the heat had to be carefully maintained.

With sadness we learned of plans to build a new village school on land adjacent to the field which was to be taken for the school drive. I always hated my time at that school! My father had lost his last real links with farming; by this time he was employed in a local car components factory. But even a rural secondary school has its compensations: I remember the fascination of watching a ewe give birth in a field next to the playground, and so conveniently at morning break!

Like most village kids, I worked on farms in the school holidays but never considered farming as a career. It would have been impossible to have grown up in such an environment and to have remained unaware of agriculture, but I can honestly say that it never seemed an attractive way of earning a living. Perhaps I knew too much.

It is easy to recount these experiences and produce an idyllic view of what 'real' farming was like, unlike today's so-called agrochemical plunder of the land. But such memories rarely have space for the harshness of country life. As village kids we knew that animals were bred for meat; we knew that the all-pervading stink of the knacker's lorry was part of life and we knew that working on farms was no holiday. Yet, when eventually I went to work in Coventry, I found that our country knowledge was not universal. 'Where are you from then?' asked one of my new colleagues. I named my village to which he replied, 'So you're a clod, why aren't you working on a farm instead of coming here and taking our jobs?'

I quickly learned that there was a difference between 'townies' and 'clods', and that many people saw the countryside in a very different way. That there was a gulf between our life styles could not be denied, but I resented the implications of the label 'clod'. I felt indignation at the suggestion that farm work was easy and fit only for the village idiot. I knew that people from my school had gone to agricultural college and that the received wisdom of my father was not that of a fool.

Later, as an undergraduate, I became concerned by the way that images of the countryside are used in the press and by advertisers. 'Down on the farm' is often a term of mild abuse or amusement, to be called a farm labourer a much used put-down. Such terms only serve to reinforce the growing gulf between farm and city.

I undertook *Farmwork* because I wanted to document the everyday life and work of people who are employed on farms. By using photography I wanted to make the work of farming more visible and, I hoped, challenge some of the romantic myths. I wanted the photography to be as neutral as possible; I did not want to adopt a partisan stance, neither wishing to criticise nor promote farming. I felt that my limited exposure to the industry was helpful, but I knew little about modern agriculture, so the photography was preceded by a period of research and familiarisation with the arguments surrounding the industry.

Documentary photography implies some sort of neutrality and impartiality, but there are always choices to be made. I do not claim to have seen, or photographed, every aspect of British agriculture, and I have obviously chosen what to photograph and what to leave out. I was not refused access to anything and was able to photograph anywhere I pleased. My approach was the well-known 'fly on the wall' technique. I wanted to be as unobtrusive as possible and never asked for particular scenes to be set up or staged for the camera. I feel that it is very important for photographers to explain what they are doing and why. All the people in the photographs knew why I was there. To have used any other approach would have seemed dishonest; even so I did experience some mis-understanding. During one of my first trips I was threatened with physical violence by a group of potato pickers. This job has traditionally been the preserve of women, but the changing employment situation has led to many men joining the gangs. When I appeared on the field with a camera there was a considerable amount of disquiet. I learned some days after that local DHSS officials had been photographing gangs of casual workers and using the photographs as evidence in prosecutions.

During one of my first attempts to photograph harvest in action, a farmer came roaring across his field in a Range Rover, stopped close to me, jumped out and said, 'You're not from Friends of the Earth, are you?' To which I replied 'No', and mentioned that I had phoned the previous evening to arrange the visit. He jumped back into the vehicle and sped away.

On the whole, the photography was very enjoyable and full of amusing incidents. I remember driving across to the west Wales coast to photograph the New Zealand 'Golden Shears' sheep shearing champion at work on a farm. It had rained during the night and the shearing was called off. On my way home I noticed a large flock of dry sheep in a roadside pen waiting to be sheared. I stopped and asked if I could photograph and the farmers agreed. Later, one of them asked if I was interested in photographing dipping; he explained that it would be after breakfast and that I was welcome to join them. We walked up the hill to the farm house. The men were shown into the kitchen and large pots of tea were produced. I was taken through to another room where there was a large table set with two places. The two farmers sat at either end and a sofa was drawn up for me. It must have been an amusing sight because I was seated considerably lower than the table which was at about chin height! It was a wonderful breakfast.

Most of these photographs were taken in 1985. By the end of that year I had travelled about 10,000 miles and produced nearly 12,000 negatives. Although West Midlands Arts had funded the photography and research, it became obvious that the project had grown much larger than originally envisaged, so I approached ICI Fertilizers for help with the production of two exhibitions and they agreed, seeing the project as low profile arts sponsorship. ICI Fertilizers and *Farmwork* won the award for best single project from the Association of Business Sponsorship of the Arts in 1986.

Two exhibitions were produced, the first a large scale, framed exhibition of prints and text aimed at galleries and arts centres. The second exhibition was intended to be shown at more informal venues such as village halls. It is designed to travel with its own portable display system to allow for showing in virtually any location. Both exhibitions started touring in September 1986 and look set to continue into the future.

It seems to me that there are two quite different views of modern farming. It is seen as a romantic occupation, a bucolic way of life beloved by many, or it is thought of as a world full of the frantic roar of machinery and the headlong rush for higher and higher profits.

The first image feeds on ideas of tradition and regret for the loss of simple rustic existence. The second is a reaction against European politics and stresses the folly of intensive farming and over-production. Both obscure the work and people in farming, the first by not permitting people to spoil the rural idyll and the second by not allowing them to intrude into macro-economics.

There is a high degree of physical isolation inherent in modern farming. Mechanisation has reduced the numbers working on the land; now crops seem to grow themselves, and a quick glance through the window of a passing car or train confirm that little work is done in the countryside. It is possible to run an arable farm of 1000 acres or more with only three or four full-time workers who see little of each other during their working day. When such a small number of people are spread over such a large area it is not surprising that their work is not very visible.

We see the countryside as a place to escape to from the pressures of urban life, a place associated with leisure rather than work. We idealise it as part of a past golden age and hark back to a time when people worked hard and played hard, when villagers were united as one, when there was a place for everyone and everyone knew their place. We obscure history to build an image of how things should have been rather than how they were.

Patterns of a ploughed field, the colours and texture of growing crops and the rural scene have long been subjects for artists. They depict the landscape but often ignore the human labour that produced it. Where work is allowed to intrude it is idealised: technology is seen as being in opposition to the ideal of rural work. The overall effect is to obscure labour; there is little human involvement apart from the old rustic, the 'character', who is only there for decoration.

Advertisers too project an image of farming as it existed before the application of modern techniques. By using a picture of someone reaping corn by hand or of horses ploughing, manufacturers hope that their product will be distinguished from the mass-produced competition. That the label bears little resemblance to the way the goods are produced is of no interest.

But farming is about producing food, the food we buy in supermarkets or from the corner shop. We are given few clues as to its source: plastic wrappings shield us from those who picked the potatoes, pulled the onions, collected the apples and harvested the grain.

Whichever way you look, agriculture seems to be in the midst of some deep crisis. Nobody knows how great the crisis will be and few appreciate the human toll. There are many people relying on agriculture for their living; when a job is lost in the country it is often much more difficult to replace than one in town. The population of villages is changing rapidly. Now it is unusual to find a single farm worker in some villages.

There is constant talk of overproduction and of the rape of the land. Some people argue that the whole system must change; others say that market forces will dictate the shape of the industry. Either way, agriculture will survive; it has to. As an industry, it has experienced most of the crises facing other industries at the moment: mechanisation, the introduction of new technologies and changing demand for its products. There is talk of a 'new agriculture', very different to the one that we know now, with fewer and fewer people employed on the land and economies of scale producing bigger and bigger machinery and more efficient processes. Perhaps then the rural myth will hark back to the days when people drove tractors, milked cows, tended sheep and grew crops. Rest assured, the myth will see this as a better time.

Work on modern farms will continue to be highly skilled, at times unpleasant, often backbreaking and always crucial to the needs of a modern society. It is safe to assume that agriculture will still rely on people; it is also safe to suggest that their work will be hidden from the majority of the population. I hope that *Farmwork* helps to challenge this obscurity and puts people back into the agricultural landscape.

TO HAZEL

Des, manager of a large arable farm in south Warwickshire.

Clearing the front of a combine harvester. There is considerable
skill in driving a combine; the route chosen around a field avoids
the straw left lying from previous cuts.

Driver of an open combine wearing a helmet to prevent breathing
in the dust which contains the spores of funghi and which, if
inhaled, can cause 'farmer's lung'.

Refuelling a combine harvester; when the weather is right harvest
continues around the clock.

Combining barley on a large arable farm in north Warwickshire.

Loading oilseed rape into a trailer from the tanks of a combine.
Rape seed is difficult to handle; it is a small and shiny and the
trailer has to be sealed with tape to avoid losing much of the load.

Measuring the hectare/litre weight of oilseed rape in order to
calibrate the yield meter in the combine.

A farm worker checks a large grain store on a farm in
Warwickshire. When grain is stored for any length of time, there
is always the risk of attack from pests.

Checking the operation of a corn drier. If the grain is too damp it
will not be suitable for storage.

Making 'big bales' in Warwickshire, an efficient way of dealing
with large quantities of straw.

Baling straw in Berkshire where it is used for bedding in
numerous racing stables. In other areas where there is no use for
the straw it is burnt in the field.

Gas blowers attached to motorcycles burn unwanted straw and
stubble on a Warwickshire farm.

Burning straw has its dangers and must be carefully supervised to avoid accidents. Burning against the wind is always safer, but the wind can shift.

Cutting down hop vines on a mixed farm in Herefordshire.

Casual workers loading a hop-picking machine in Herefordshire.

The hops are stored in sacks prior to loading into the kiln to be
dried.

After the hops are dried they are compressed into large storage
sacks and the tops are sewn.

Workers on a Herefordshire hop farm in their living quarters
during the hop-picking season.

The driver of a pea swather in Cambridgeshire. A swather cuts
the plants, leaving them in a swathe or long pile which a second
machine picks up to then strip the plants. Modern pea vining
machines do the same job in a single pass but they are very
expensive.

A pea viner at work in Suffolk. These machines are the size of a
double-decker bus; they operate 24 hours a day with the drivers
doing a 12-hour shift.

Refuelling a pea viner in Suffolk. Most farmers share machinery
to reduce costs and usually work under contract to frozen food
producers.

The machines are thoroughly cleaned at the end of each 12-hour
shift. Compressed air blows away the debris and the whole
machine is washed by means of a portable pressure washer.

Spraying broad beans to eradicate black fly on a Pick-Your-Own
farm in Warwickshire.

A farm worker operating a potato planter in Warwickshire.

Filling the hopper of a potato planter with seed potatoes.

Adjusting a four-row potato planter in the field during a
particularly bad planting session.

A casual worker sorting potatoes before bagging on a
Warwickshire farm.

Spraying potatoes in Northamptonshire with pre-emergence
spray to control weeds. The spray kills any green plants so correct
timing is vital to avoid killing the young potato plants.

Picking new potatoes by hand on a Warwickshire farm. Picking
can be mechanised but it is still done by hand on heavy land or
where the crop does not justify the cost of a machine.

Planting Brussels sprouts in Warwickshire.

Opposite top
Loading a planting machine with Brussels sprout plants on a
large farm in north Warwickshire.
Bottom
Sitting on steel seats close to the ground, the operators pass a
plant down the chute to be planted at each ring of the bell
attached to one of the planting machine wheels.

Picking Brussels sprouts in the Vale of Evesham. At a time when
growers were receiving 50p for a 20lb net of sprouts, they were
selling in supermarkets for 38p per pound.

Morning tea break for Brussels sprout pickers in the January
snow. 'You get used to the cold; it's the wet that's really bad.'

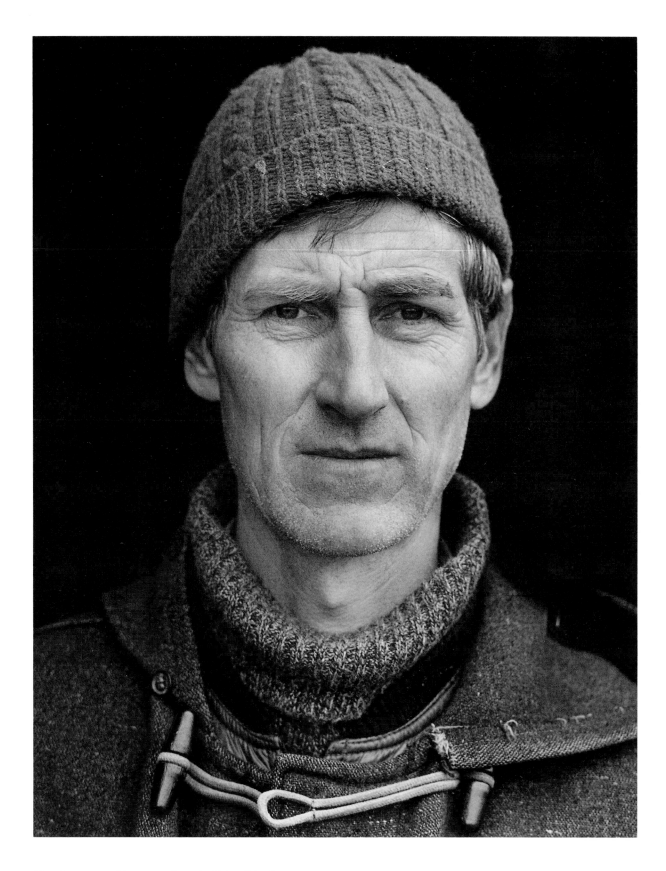

Maurice, a vegetable grower from the Vale of Evesham.

Loading cabbages for market.

Cutting cabbage on a Warwickshire vegetable farm.

Trimming swedes. The whole plant is pulled from the ground
and the roots and top slashed off with a sharp knife.

A grower in the Vale of Evesham pulling kohlrabi for the
Birmingham market.

A hot house of lettuces in the Vale of Evesham. Each lettuce is
cut by hand and immediately put into a polythene bag for delivery
to shops.

Hoeing lettuce in Warwickshire. 'The weed control didn't work,
so we have to hoe all the weeds from around the plants.'

Casual worker hoeing lettuce wearing a tee-shirt which
reads 'Cyprus the island of Venus'.

Picking raspberries in Warwickshire. On some farms the pay can
be as low as 50p per hour.

The packer and supervisor of casual workers employed picking
strawberries in Warwickshire.

A casual worker picking dessert apples in Herefordshire.

Tulip pickers take their lunch break on the edge of the tulip field, resting on bags full of the flower heads. About five million are picked and used to decorate the floats in the Spalding Tulip Time Festival.

In Lincolnshire, Kate, 75 years old, picks the heads off tulips to encourage growth of the bulb which will be lifted and sold.

Pulling salad onions in the Vale of Evesham.

Salad onions are washed and bunched before being trimmed by
hand. The smell is overpowering.

Repairing a dry stone wall in Derbyshire.

Building a field bridge in Wales.

Trimming a hedge using a flail cutter.

Laying a hedge in Derbyshire. Hedge laying has seen something
of a revival in recent years.

Repairing a potato planter is all in a day's work. Often there is no
time to call a mechanic and the farm worker has to keep the
machinery running.

At the start of harvest, machinery is overhauled and repairs done.
A modern farm worker has to be versatile; welding is now one of
the skills thought of as part of the job.

The farmer, machinery agents and salesman discuss the relative
merits of a new plough, on trial on a Warwickshire arable farm.

Attaching a towing bracket to a large tractor.

Mowing grass for silage in Devon.

Commissioning a new big bale machine on a Warwickshire farm.

Preparing to remove a bogged tractor.

Steve, a general farm worker from Warwickshire.

Preparing to start work with a subsoil plough attached to a 300hp
tractor.

Moving muck before spreading it on a field to be planted with potatoes.

A forage harvester picking up grass for silage in stormy weather.

Tying the ends of big bale silage bags. The grass is left to ferment
inside the bags which can be stored outside and used when
needed.

Grazing dairy cows in Warwickshire.

Driving the cows back to the field on a Warwickshire dairy farm.

A relief milker at a dairy unit.

Testing for mastitis before milking on a Leicestershire dairy
farm. The first milk is drawn off through a sieve into a cup where
it can be inspected for the lumps characteristic of mastitis.

Attaching the cluster to a difficult cow; she had a torn teat and
was in some pain; not to have milked would have added to her
discomfort.

Mr Wilson, cattle breeder.

Collecting milk from the mobile tank in Devon. Small farms
often cannot afford a refrigerated bulk tank, so they use lagged,
mobile tanks which are towed to the end of the farm road.

Feeding calves on a Warwickshire dairy farm.

Injecting anaesthetic before dehorning a calf on a
Northamptonshire beef unit.

After the anaesthetic the horn buds are burnt out by a gas-driven
poker.

Trimming the hoof of a pedigree bull, taking great care not to cut
the blood vessels just below the surface of the hoof.

Driving sheep from field to farm for sorting, in Staffordshire.

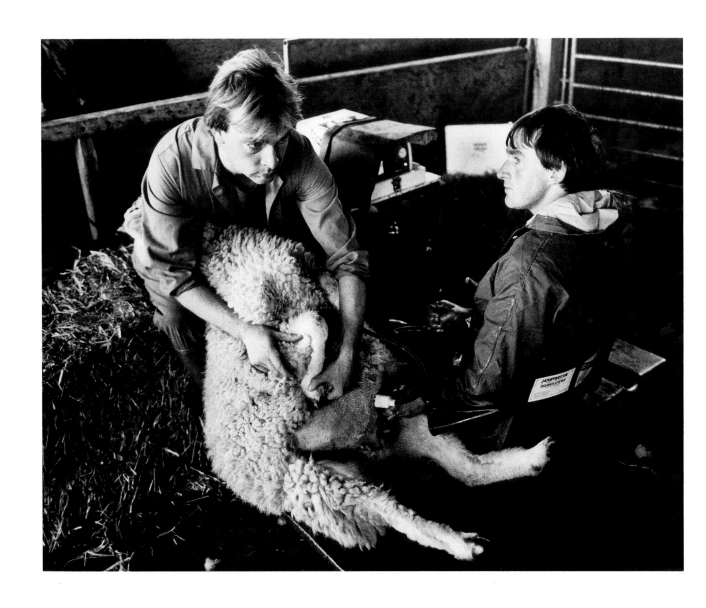

Scanning a pregnant ewe to ascertain the number of lambs she is
carrying.

Dipping sheep in a Warwickshire sheep unit. This has to be done
twice a year to control sheep scab.

Danny Wild checking his flock on the Pennines above Rochdale
in Lancashire.

A difficult lambing on the moors above Rochdale. The second
lamb needed help from the shepherd; the size of its horn buds
made it a difficult birth.

A shepherdess tending a ewe with her new-born lamb.

Fitting the skin of a still-born lamb on to an orphaned lamb to
ensure its adoption.

Inoculating lambs on a Warwickshire sheep unit against orf, an
infectious form of dermatitis.

Supplementing the feed of a new-born lamb.

Mr Pugh, a Welsh sheep farmer.

Sorting sheep on a Staffordshire mixed farm.

A shearing gang in action on a Northamptonshire farm.

A sheep shearer from New Zealand.

Feeding sheep on a traditional mixed farm.

Injecting sheep against foot rot.

Trimming the feet of an ewe, held still in a cradle, before
dipping.

Feeding silage to sheep in Warwickshire in January.

The late Richard Seabrook, freelance farmer, Suffolk.

Rosamund Young with her organic breeding sows in
Warwickshire

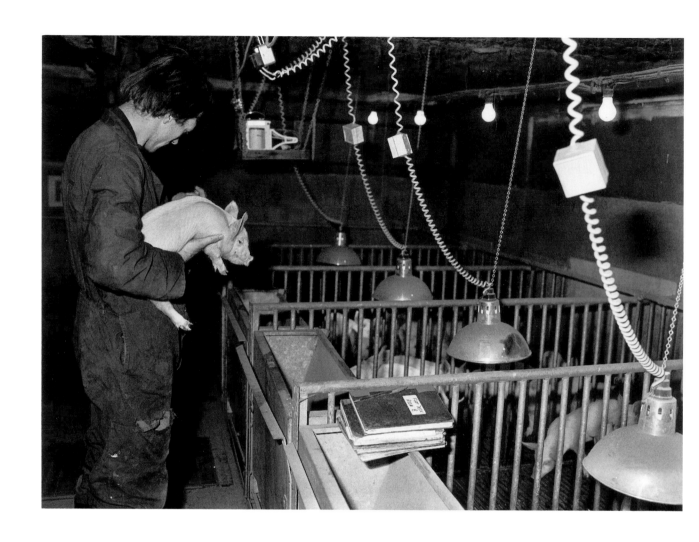

Checking the health of a pig in an intensive rearing unit.

Sorting pigs for market.

Drawing a sample of milk from a sow about to farrow.

Sows in adjoining sties on a Warwickshire farm.

Driving turkeys on a Warwickshire poultry farm.

'Littering' a deep litter turkey house in Warwickshire.

Plucking 'farm fresh' turkeys for Christmas.

Restocking a battery rearing house on a large poultry farm.

Sorting eggs on a conveyor belt at a packing station attached to a
large farm.

Round the ring at Banbury market.

A selling ring at the annual sheep fair at Rugby market.

A selling ring at Banbury market.

Stockman, Banbury market.

Steaming animals just unloaded and ready for sale at Banbury
market, the largest cattle market in Europe.

A prize ram for sale at Rugby market.

After the judging at the annual sheep fair at Rugby market.

Preparing for judging at the Royal Show.

The county show, Kirkwall, Orkney.